# Nelson Readers
## Series editor: Lewis Jo

A library of graded readers for s
reluctant native readers. The boo
Structure, vocabulary, idiom and
principles laid down in detail in
The books are listed below acco
300 words and appropriate struc
words, 5: 2000 words and 6: 250    ....... ....... ..... .... .... ...........
accompanied by a cassette.

Nelson Readers Level 2

# Dangerous Earth

## Jane Homeshaw

Nelson

Thomas Nelson and Sons Ltd
Nelson House, Mayfield Road
Walton-on-Thames, Surrey
KT12 5PL, UK

51 York Place
Edinburgh
EH1 3JD, UK

Thomas Nelson (Hong Kong) Ltd
Toppan Building 10/F
22a Westlands Road
Quarry Bay, Hong Kong

© Jane Homeshaw 1984

First published by Collins ELT 1984

Reprinted: 1987, 1988, 1990

ISBN 0-00-370157-3

This edition first published by
Thomas Nelson and Sons Ltd 1992

ISBN 0-17-556427-2
NPN 9 8 7 6 5 4 3 2

We are grateful to Frank Lane Agency for
permission to reproduce the photograph which
appears on the cover.
Cover design by Dan Lim.
Maps and diagrams drawn by Gina Smart.

Printed in Great Britain
by Bell and Bain Ltd., Glasgow

Only the wind moved in that high dead place. There were no people, no birds and no trees. White snow topped the mountain. The only colour was brown.

Brown stones in an empty world. They ran, like a chocolate river, down from the top of the mountain.

From far away, there came the sound of a car. It grew louder as it neared the place. The car stopped and two young men got out.

"I can't believe it, Juan," said the driver. "You say there was a town here a week ago?"

"Yes," said Juan. "The town of Yungay. I lived here, Mr Wilson."

"Call me Mark." He eyed four small points on the ground. "What are those?"

"Those are the tops of the four tallest trees in the town. They stood in the market place. 20 000 bodies are here, under the stones."

"Tell me about it," said Mark. "I'm a newspaper man." He took out a notebook and pen . . .

# The Yungay Earthquake

"I was in school," said Juan. "On the blackboard, in big white letters was the date – May 31st 1970. The letters started to dance in front of my eyes."

"Were you asleep?"

"No. I looked out of the window. There was a noise, like a big lorry in the street. But outside there were only a few empty cars."

"What made the noise?"

"It came from the ground. The cars started to jump up and down. Then the classroom clock fell off the wall and the window broke.

"I was afraid. I ran out of school and into the street. As I ran, the houses started to fall down. The ground moved under my feet. I knew then . . ."

"Knew what?"

"I knew that it was an earthquake. I ran to the fields. I could hear bangs and screams behind me. I only turned round when I got to the second field.

"I couldn't believe my eyes. Nearly all the buildings were on the ground. In front of me, the earth moved up and down like a sea."

"What did you do?"

"Nothing, for a while. Then I heard another sound, like great guns. It came from the mountains. I looked up and the nearest mountain began to fly at me!

"I ran away and swam across the river. On the other side, I started to run again. A great wind carried me along. Then earth and snow fell on top of me . . ."

"Snow?"

"Yes. Mountain snow. The earthquake broke off a large piece of the mountain."

Mark turned back a few pages in his notebook. "It says here it was 800 metres wide and 1½ kilometres long. Did all that fall on the town and the river? The mountain's a long way away."

"15 kilometres," said Juan.

"Oh, yes . . . I have a note here. It fell 15 kilometres in 4 minutes. It doesn't seem

*The earthquake in Yungay, Peru on 31st May 1970.*

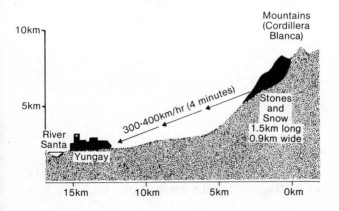

possible.''

''I know it wasn't long,'' said Juan. ''When the mountain fell on the river, there was a wall of water 14 metres high. It escaped down into the sea, but on the way down it killed a lot of people here in Peru.''

''How many died?'' asked Mark.

''50 000 died and another 100 000 people were hurt. Nearly a million lost their homes – that's one out of every 13 people in Peru. I think it was the worst earthquake ever.''

Mark looked in his notebook again.

''There was an earthquake in China in 1556. It killed 830 000 people. In 1923, in Japan, 142 000 people died.''

''Why do earthquakes happen?'' asked Juan.

''Come with me tonight,'' said Mark. ''I'm going to try to find out.''

## What Makes an Earthquake?

That evening, in a room full of books, an old man with white hair handed them a picture.

''From the outside of the earth to the middle is more than 6000 kilometres,'' he said. ''As you know, the middle of the earth is very hot. A car body would change to a watery liquid there.''

"Like snow, Mr Quevedo?'' asked Juan. ''If you put snow in a warm place, it changes to water. And glass and iron become liquid when they're too hot.''

"That's right,'' said the old scientist. ''Inside the earth is hot, heavy, liquid iron. The outside of the earth is a lighter rock. It stays on top of the liquid.''

"Water moves,'' said Mark suddenly. ''Does liquid iron move in the same way?''

"Yes,'' said Mr Quevedo. ''That's how earthquakes happen. Come into the bathroom and I'll show you.''

In the bathroom, Juan and Mark filled the bath with water. Mr Quevedo brought two thin, light plates and a cupful of sand.

"Put the plates on the water,'' he told them. ''Now each of you take a spoonful of sand. Put your spoonful on the side of your plate. Now move your hands up and down in the water.''

"The plates are moving too,'' said Juan.

"The plates are touching,'' cried Mark. ''And . . . yes . . . the small hills of sand have fallen down.''

"It's like the Yungay earthquake – when the mountain fell down,'' said Juan. ''Does that mean that Peru is on the side of a plate? I don't understand. What plate?''

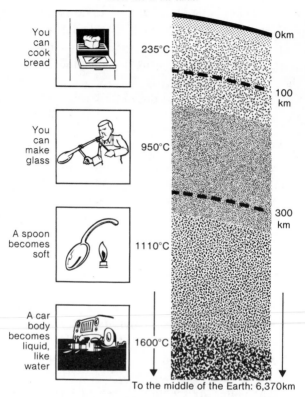

You can cook bread — 235°C — 0km

You can make glass — 950°C — 100 km

A spoon becomes soft — 1110°C — 300 km

A car body becomes liquid, like water — 1600°C

To the middle of the Earth: 6,370km

"Come back to the other room," said Mr Quevedo. "I want to show you a book."

A few minutes later, he said: "This picture shows you where the world's earthquakes happen."

"Were there earthquakes on all these points?"

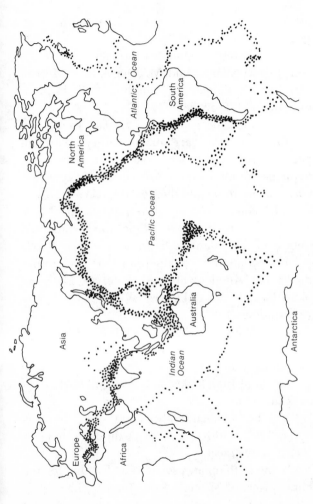

*All earthquakes round the world 1961–67.*

asked Mark after a time. "It doesn't seem possible."

"There are 1 million earthquakes round the world every year," said Mr Quevedo. "Most of them aren't dangerous. Buildings fall down in only about 120 of them."

"How often do people die?" asked Juan.

"One or two earthquakes every year kill people. An earthquake like ours last week happens less often – perhaps every 10 or 20 years. Cars kill more people than earthquakes do."

"The points seem to make lines," said Mark with his eyes on the book. "One runs through the middle of the Atlantic Ocean."

"Here's another," said Juan. "It goes round the Pacific. And look at South America. There's a black line all along the west side. Peru is in the very middle of it."

"Here's another book," said Mr Quevedo. "Let me find the right page . . . This shows all the plates round the world."

Mark and Juan looked at the second book, then back at the first.

"The line of earthquakes is the same shape as the plates," said Mark. "So earthquakes happen where plates meet."

"Some of the plates seem to be fighting for the same piece of space," said Juan. "The West Atlantic plate is touching the Nazca plate. What's going to happen to Peru in the future?"

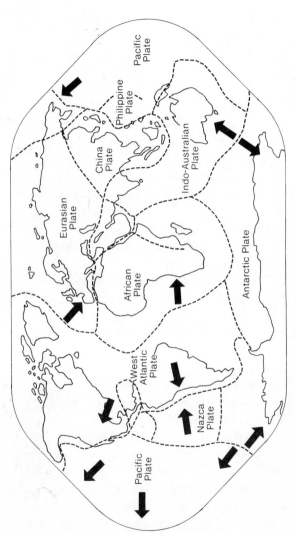

*Plates round the world.*

"Come to lunch tomorrow, and I'll tell you," said Mr Quevedo.

## How to Make a New Ocean

Mr Quevedo was in the kitchen when the boys arrived.

"The other food is ready," he told them. "But I waited for you before I cooked the potatoes."

"Why?" asked Juan.

"You see that the water is cold, and the potatoes are staying below the water?"

"Yes."

Mr Quevedo put a match to the fire.

"See what happens when the water becomes hot."

They waited for a few minutes, then Juan said, "The potatoes are moving. They're climbing up to the top of the water."

"But look now," said Mark. "When they meet the cold air, they become colder and fall down again."

"Now they're getting hot again," said Juan. "They're shooting up to the top."

"Some small pieces have broken away from the

14

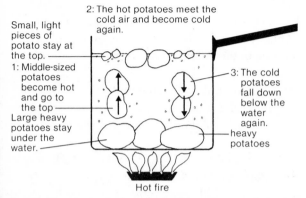

2: The hot potatoes meet the cold air and become cold again.

Small, light pieces of potato stay at the top.

1: Middle-sized potatoes become hot and go to the top

Large heavy potatoes stay under the water.

3: The cold potatoes fall down below the water again.

heavy potatoes

Hot fire

*As cold things become hotter, they also become larger, and, for their size, lighter.*

larger ones,'' said Mark. ''They're staying at the top.''

''That's right,'' said Mr Quevedo. ''The smaller pieces are lighter, so they stay on top. The larger, heavier pieces stay under the water near the fire. Then, as they get hotter, they also get bigger. They become, *for their size*, less heavy. The lighter potatoes move to the top. There, they become smaller, colder and heavier – so they fall down again.''

''Is the middle of the earth like that?'' asked Juan suddenly. ''You said last night there was a lot of hot, heavy, liquid iron under the earth.''

''I know what you mean,'' said Mark. ''The lighter stone moves to the top and becomes land.''

''It does if it can find a way out,'' said Mr

Quevedo. "In a lot of places the stone – or rock – is very thick. The liquid rock can't get out.

"There are some places where it can escape. In the middle of the Atlantic Ocean, the rock plate is very thin.

"Hot light liquid rock came up from under the earth. It broke the old thin plate into two pieces – the West Atlantic plate and the African plate."

"When did all this happen?" asked Mark.

"It began 135 million years ago," said Mr Quevedo. "It's still happening. The liquid rock comes to the top, meets the cold water, and changes to hard, heavy rock. South America is still moving away from Africa like this."

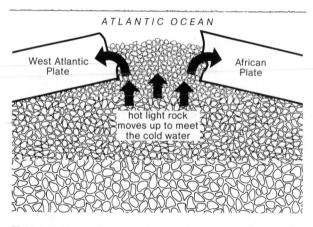

*The hot, light rock climbs up and reaches the cold water of the Atlantic Ocean. It becomes hard rock and moves the old plate away.*

"Where will South America go?" asked Juan. "Last night we learned that it's touching the Nazca plate in the Pacific Ocean."

"South America is eating the Nazca plate," said Mr Quevedo. "Just like we're going to eat those potatoes. They're ready."

## How Plates Move

After the meal, Juan asked his question again.

"Where will South America go?"

"There are two possible answers," said Mr Quevedo.

"Two?" said Mark. "I can't think of *one*."

"If the road in front of you is closed, you must sometimes go back," said Juan.

"But that isn't possible," said Mark. "The new sea floor under the Atlantic will stop it."

"Look at this piece of paper," said Mr Quevedo. "If I hold the left side with my left hand . . . and if I move the right side with my right hand . . . What happens?"

"The left side of the paper goes up in the air like a line of mountains!" said Mark.

"The Andes mountains are on the left side of

South America!'' shouted Juan. ''Did the Andes grow like that?''

''Yes,'' said Mr Quevedo. ''And that's not all. Land plate rock is lighter than sea plate rock. It must always stay on top.''

''Like oil stays on top of water?''

''Yes. The heavier Nazca sea plate is moving down under Peru. As it moves down, it becomes liquid rock again.''

''Just a minute,'' said Mark. ''We know that the South American plate can't move to the west or east. But suppose it moves to the north or the south, so that it passes the Nazca plate?''

''Some plates can do that,'' said Mr Quevedo. ''That's happening in the Middle East. There, part of the Eurasian plate is moving south, while

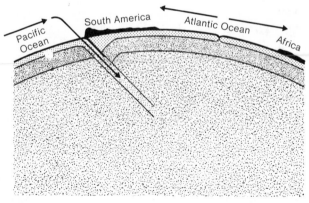

*The South American plate is 'eating' the Nazco plate of the Pacific Ocean.*

the Arabian plate is moving north.

"The South American plate can't do that," he finished. "It can only move to the west."

"How fast does it move?" asked Juan.

"Very slowly," smiled Mr Quevedo. "About 1 centimetre every year."

"How old is the earth?" asked Mark suddenly.

"4500 million years old."

"So, in all that time, it's possible for plates to move a long way."

"You're right," said Mr Quevedo. "The plates have moved about the earth. I'll get some pictures that will show you."

*In the East Mediterranean, plates move past one another.*

# Fossils

"Where was all the land at the beginning of the earth?" asked Mark.

"We don't know," said Mr Quevedo, "but here are some pictures of it 500 million years ago."

Juan looked at *b*.

"North America and Europe are in the place of Africa today," he said. "South America and Africa are nearer the south. And look at Antarctica and Australia! They're up in the middle."

"Was it hot there then?" asked Mark.

"Perhaps hotter than now," said Mr Quevedo. "There were no large, cold, snowy lands at the very north and south – so the water was less than cold. Fewer cold oceans means warmer land."

"Maybe Antarctica had hot weather there. Perhaps there were hot-weather plants and animals on it," said Mark.

"There were," said Mr Quevedo. "Scientists have found their shapes in the rocks of today's Antarctica."

"Do you mean fossils?" asked Mark.

"What are fossils?" questioned Juan.

"When plants and animals die, their soft parts go first," began Mr Quevedo. "Their hard parts often stay on the ground for a long time."

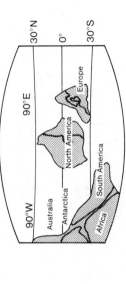

a. The world today

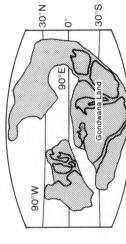

b. 510 ± 40 million years ago

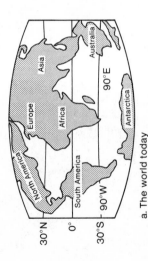

c. 380 ± 30 million years ago

d. 340 ± 30 million years ago

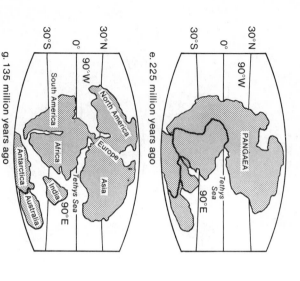

e. 225 million years ago

f. 180 million years ago

g. 135 million years ago

h. 65 million years ago

"I know," said Juan. "You often see the hard woody shape of a leaf on the ground after the soft green part has gone."

"As the years pass, more earth or sand falls on top of the leaf. After a longer time, perhaps hundreds of thousands of years, the earth and sand become hard rock. You can still see the shape of the dead leaf in the rock . . ."

"And that's a fossil!" finished Juan.

"Can you date fossils?" asked Mark suddenly.

"Yes," said Mr Quevedo. "We know when different kinds of plants and animals lived, so we know the age of fossils."

"If you can date a fossil, you can also date the rock round it," said Mark. "So if you find fossils of hot-weather plants and animals in Antarctica, you know when Antarctica was in a hot part of the earth."

"Is that how you scientists know the land has moved?" asked Juan. "You looked at the fossils?"

"It's one way. But there are other ways too."

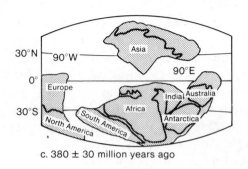

c. 380 ± 30 million years ago

# The Story in the Rocks

"Look at the picture of the earth 380 million years ago," said Mr Quevedo.

"The earth has changed a lot in 130 million years," said Juan. "North America and Europe are now in the south-west. South America, Africa, India, Australia and Antarctica are all together in one big piece of land in the southern half of the world. Asia is in the north. Why are there breaks in the line at the top of Northern Asia?"

"A lot of Asia was under sea water," said Mr Quevedo.

"Do you know that because of the fossils?" asked Mark.

"Yes. A lot of the fossils are of fish, and other sea animals."

"How do you know that South America and

24

Africa were one land?'' asked Juan. ''Is that because of the fossils too?''

''Partly,'' said Mr Quevedo. ''You can find the story of South-East Brazil and South-West Africa in their rocks.

''500 million years ago, they had the same very old rock. Later, the land in both places was under sea water at the same time. Sand fell on top of the rock and became hard sandstone.

''350 million years ago, Brazil and South-West Africa were at the southern end of the world. It was very cold. The cold broke the rocks into small pieces.

''When the land moved north again, it became warmer. Thick woods grew up. You can find the same kind of fossils in both places.

''After the trees came a dry time. The hot winds brought dry sand. The land moved under water, and more sand fell on top of it.

''Then, 150 million years ago, the plate broke into two. Hot liquid rock came up from the middle of the earth, and began to make a new sea floor. South America started to move away from Africa.''

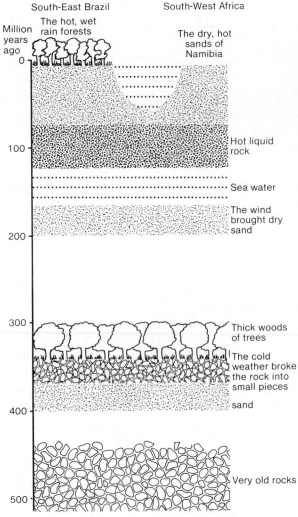

*The story of the rocks of South America and Africa.*

South-East Brazil · South-West Africa

The hot, wet rain forests · The dry, hot sands of Namibia

Million years ago

0

100 — Hot liquid rock

Sea water

The wind brought dry sand

200

300 — Thick woods of trees

The cold weather broke the rock into small pieces

sand

400

Very old rocks

500

From D.H. and M.P. Tarling. 'The Continental Drift' Pelican 1972

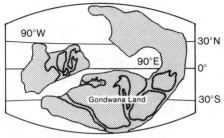

d. 340 ± 30 million years ago

# Pangaea and After

"What happened in other places?" asked Mark. "In picture *d*, it seems that all the land on earth is meeting together."

"That's what happened," said Juan. "You can see it in *e*. 225 million years ago, there was one great piece of land . . . one big continent!"

"Scientists today call it the continent of

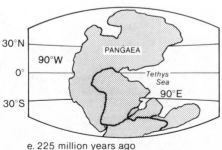

e. 225 million years ago

Pangaea. The word 'Pangaea' means 'all the world'.'' said Mr Quevedo. ''And they call the sea near it, the Tethys Sea.''

Mark said, ''In the northern half of the world, there was North America, Europe and Asia. In the southern half, there was South America, Africa, India, Australia and Antarctica.''

''That's nearly the same as today,'' said Juan.

''Not India,'' said Mark. ''India is now part of Asia. What happened there?''

''180 million years ago, Pangaea began to break into two continents,'' said Mr Quevedo. ''We call the northern continent Laurasia and the southern continent Gondwana Land.

''A new sea floor began to open between India and Australia-Antarctica.

''135 million years ago, India became an island. It started to move north as the Indian Ocean grew wider. At the same time, the Atlantic Ocean opened between South America and

f. 180 million years ago

28

Africa. The Tethys Sea became smaller. Its eastern end began to close.

"65 million years ago, the Tethys Sea closed as Africa moved round and started to meet Southern Europe and West Asia. This made the Alps – the mountains that are in Southern Europe. We now call the Tethys Sea the Mediterranean.

"A little later, India touched Southern Asia. This made the world's biggest and newest mountains – the Himalayas.

"At the same time, Australia left Antarctica

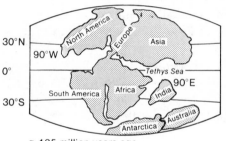

g. 135 million years ago

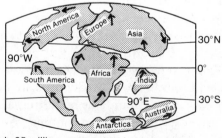

h. 65 million years ago

and started to move north. The world began to have its present shape.''


# The Shape of the Future


''What's going to happen in the future?''

''What do you mean, Juan?''

''We know what's happened to the earth in the past. Do we know what will happen to it in the future?''

''We know some things,'' said Mr Quevedo. ''We know that the Red Sea is growing wider. And we know that the Arabian Sea is beginning to change into an ocean.''

''How do we know?''

''The Red Sea isn't very deep. Scientists can go down under water and look.''

''What's happening to Africa?''

''It's still moving north. One day, it will meet Europe.''

''What will happen to the Mediterranean?''

''There won't be a Mediterranean Sea any more. The Atlas Mountains of North Africa will meet the Alps of Southern Europe. Together, they will make some new, very high mountains –

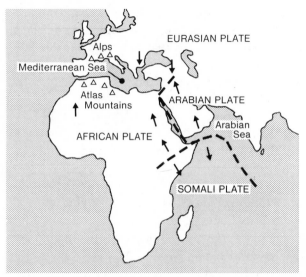

*The Arabian Sea is beginning to make a new ocean.*

perhaps bigger than the Himalayas.''

"What's going to happen here, in the Americas?'' asked Juan.

"As America moves west, the Pacific Ocean is becoming smaller,''said Mr Quevedo. "A lot of the sea floor is moving down into the middle of the earth. That isn't only happening on this side of the ocean. It's also happening on the other side – near Japan and Indonesia, and down near Australia too.

"At some future date, perhaps in another 50 million years, the Rocky Mountains of North America will meet Japan. The Andes of South

31

America will meet the Philippines and Tonga."

"I was in California last year," said Mark. "Monday April 14th 1969. I remember the date. Some of the Californians were afraid. They drove up into the hills and waited."

"Why?" asked Juan.

"I asked them the same question," said Mark.

"They told me, 'Today, California is going to break away from North America and fall into the sea'."

"What happened?"

"Nothing," said Mark. "At night, they all went back home again."

"They were wrong about only one thing," said Mr Quevedo.

"What was that?"

"The date. California is on the Pacific plate. The other parts of North America are on the North American plate. The Pacific plate is moving past the other. In 60 million years, California will fall into the middle of the earth – just north of Alaska.

"There are a lot of earthquakes in California," said Juan. "You read about them in the newspapers all the time."

"The most famous one happened in San Francisco in 1906," said Mark. "700 people died."

"50 000 people died here in Peru last week," cried Juan. "My mother and father were two of them."

"I'm very sorry," said Mr Quevedo. "Scientists all over the world are working on the question of earthquakes. They're tryng to stop them."

"How can you stop earthquakes?" asked Mark.

For an answer, Mr Quevedo got up and went out of the room. He came back with two boxes of matches.


# Can You Stop an Earthquake?


"Juan can have one box of matches – he's the North American plate. Mark can have the other – he's California."

"What shall we do?"

"Find the side of the box that has the sand-paper," said Mr Quevedo. "Good. Now I want you to put the two boxes together. The two sandpaper sides must touch."

"Shall we still hold the boxes?"

"Yes. Now I'm going to put a small piece of money on top of each box. Mark – try to move your box past Juan's. The boxes must still touch, but I want the money to stay on top of each box."

"It's difficult," said Mark. "The sandpaper is holding the two boxes together."

"You're a strong young man," said Mr Quevedo. "Try harder."

Mark tried again. His box moved quickly past Juan's, but both pieces of money shot up in the air and landed on the table.

"Mark was *too* strong!" laughed Juan.

"*You* try," said Mark.

They changed places, but the same thing happened.

"It's the sandpaper," said Juan. "It isn't soft enough."

"Just a minute," said Mark. "Can I get something from your kitchen, Mr Quevedo?"

"Of course," smiled the scientist. "I think Mark's found the answer."

Mark came back with a bottle of oil. He put a little on each of the sandpaper sides. Then he tried to move his box again. This time, it moved easily, and the money stayed still.

"But you can't put oil into the ground," said Juan. "It's too expensive."

"Not oil," said Mr Quevedo. "Water. That's cheap."

"Have they tried it?" asked Mark.

"In some places," said Mr Quevedo. "Of course, it's difficult. You must put enough water in the right places."

"Can we try it here, in Peru?" asked Juan.

"No," said Mr Quevedo sadly. "The plates aren't both moving the same way, as they are in North America. The South American plate is moving west, and the Nazca plate must move east under it. We can only do one thing – we must learn to build better buildings."

"Like they do in Japan?" asked Mark.

"Yes, but of course, buildings like that are expensive."

"And Peru is a poor country," finished Juan.

## Volcanoes

"Peru doesn't only have earthquakes," said Mark. "You also have volcanoes, don't you?"

"I've visited the volcano at Arequipa," said Juan. "It's a round hill, nearly 6000 metres high."

"Is it alive?" asked Mark. "Does hot liquid rock still shoot out of it?"

"In Peru, all things are possible," said Mr Quevedo.

"Do you always find volcanoes where there are earthquakes?"

"Very often," said Mr Quevedo. "You often find them where the side of a plate – like the Nazca plate here – is moving down under the earth."

"What happens?"

Mr Quevedo took a pencil and paper.

"I'll show you," he said. "As the rock of the Nazca plate moves deeper under the earth, it becomes hotter and changes to liquid. Air and water escape from it, and it breaks into pieces. Some of the smaller pieces of rock move up with the air and water . . ."

*How volcanoes happen.*

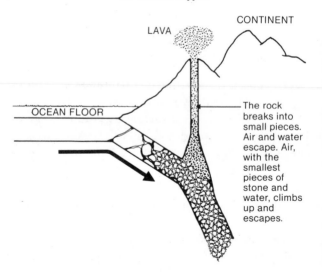

LAVA

CONTINENT

OCEAN FLOOR

The rock breaks into small pieces. Air and water escape. Air, with the smallest pieces of stone and water, climbs up and escapes.

"Like the smallest pieces of potato that you cooked?" asked Juan.

"That's right," said the old scientist. "If they can find a weak place in the land rock, the liquid rock, water and air – we call it lava – shoots up into the upper air. That's a volcano.

"Often, it shoots up fast, and takes a lot of land rock with it, high into the air."

"The worst volcano in modern times was Krakatoa, wasn't it?" asked Mark. "I read about it. It happened in 1883 in Indonesia."

"Yes. Indonesia has over 70 volcanoes – more than any other country. I have a book about Krakatoa. Here. Let me find the page . . . Oh, here it is. Read it for us, Juan."

"Krakatoa was a small island – about the size of the English market town of Cambridge," read Juan. "It's between Sumatra and Java. The eruption of its volcano happened at 10 o'clock in the morning of 27th August, 1883. It killed 36 380 people. They lost 163 villages.

"The eruption threw rocks 54 kilometres up into the air. Ten days later, small pieces of lava fell down to earth 5000 kilometres away.

"Four hours after the eruption, people heard its noise 5000 kilometres away, on the island of Rodrigues, in the Indian Ocean, east of Africa.

"They said, 'It sounded like heavy guns.'

"The eruption left an open space about 4 kilometres across. Krakatoa Island lost millions of tonnes of rock . . ."

"The great wall of China is more than 3 000 kilometres long. It's between 5–20 metres high, and up to 16 metres wide. You could build 400 Great Walls of China with the lost rock from Krakatoa."

"That *is* a lot!" said Mark. "Mr Quevedo, why does Indonesia have more than 70 volcanoes? Is it on the side of a plate?"

"Three plates meet in and round Indonesia," said Mr Quevedo. "The China plate, the Indo-Australian plate and the Philippine plate. They're all fighting for the same piece of space.

"Look. Here's another picture of the earth. It shows where the land volcanoes are."

"There *are* a lot in Indonesia," said Juan. "And in Japan . . . and here, on the western side of America. Are these all places where the sea floor is going down under the earth?"

"Yes. Because the rock on continents is lighter, it stays on top. It's the heavier stone of the ocean floor that must go down under it."

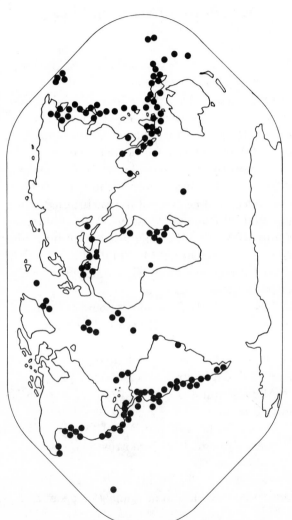

*Where volcanoes happen.*

# Mountains Under the Sea

"You talked about *land* volcanoes," said Mark. "Are there also sea volcanoes?"

"Of course," said Mr Quevedo. "Do you remember when we talked about how to make a new sea floor? The hot lava comes up to make a new sea floor – those are volcanoes too.

"Of course, we don't know where all the under-water volcanoes are, because the oceans are too deep. Some parts of the Pacific Ocean are more than 10 kilometres deep. You could lose Mount Everest – the highest mountain on earth – in the ocean near the Philppines."

"Are there real mountains under the sea?" asked Juan.

"Yes," said Mr Quevedo. "Some of them are higher than Mount Everest. There's one mountain in the Pacific Ocean – between Samoa and New Zealand – 9½ kilometres high. And there's still 640 metres of sea above it."

"All these numbers!" said Juan. "I'm sorry. I must go home to bed."

"Go home, both of you," said Mr Quevedo. "You can come back tomorrow if you like."

"Tomorrow?"

"Yes, we've talked a lot about rocks. But we haven't said much about animals or people . . . yet."

# Plates, Animals and People

"Have you heard about the dinosaurs?" asked Mr Quevedo the next evening.

"They were great big animals that lived millions of years ago," said Juan. "Some were over 40 metres long. Some of them could fly."

"When did they live on earth?" asked Mark.

"They began about 200 million years ago," said Mr Quevedo. "They walked, or flew round the world for 135 million years. Man has only been here for 2 million years."

"200 million years ago . . ." said Mark. "The land was one big continent then, wasn't it?"

"Pangaea," said Juan.

"At about that time, Pangaea began to break up into smaller continents," said Mr Quevedo. "A lot of the land was under warm water. Dinosaurs liked that. Fish liked it too. There were lots of different kinds of fish. Then, about 65 million years ago, the fish and the dinosaurs began to die."

"What happened to the land at that time?" asked Mark.

"I remember," said Juan. "New sea floors began to grow. South America left Africa and North America started to move away from Europe."

"That's right," said Mr Quevedo. "The sea

water near or on the continents went to fill the new oceans. A lot of the fish died. The dinosaurs died too.

"Now there were new kinds of animals – animals that liked dry land. A lot had warm blood . . ."

"Like man?" asked Juan.

"Yes – but there were many animals with warm blood before man," said Mr Quevedo. "Dinosaur babies came from eggs – like young birds today. Mother and father birds must spend a lot of time with their eggs. The eggs must be warm, so the birds can't leave them. It's too dangerous.

"The new dry-land animals found a better way. The young stayed with their mother – in warm pockets of hair in front of their bodies."

"Like kangaroos in Australia?" shouted Juan. "The mothers jump along and look for food and carry their babies with them."

"Yes," said Mr Quevedo. "And remember, at that time there were land-bridges between South America, Antarctica and Australia. There were kangaroo-like animals in South America once."

"What happened to them?"

"In the northern continents, the animals found another better way. They kept them *inside* their bodies. The babies only came out when they were strong and ready to run.

"After a few million more years, North

America met South America. The new northern animals crossed over into South America. Most of the kangaroo-like animals died.''

''What's happening now, in Australia?'' asked Juan. ''The Europeans took a lot of their animals there.''

''Yes,'' said Mr Quevedo. ''A lot of the kangaroo-like animals are dying. The Australians are trying to keep them alive. But maybe it's too late.''

''We can learn a lot from the story of the earth,'' said Juan suddenly.

''What do you mean?'' asked Mark.

''We can learn that it's better to keep some animals away from others,'' said Juan.

''Away from man, too,'' said Mark. ''Man mustn't use all the land for his towns, or cut down all the trees so the animals can't live in them.''

''We can also learn about earthquakes and volcanoes,'' said Juan. ''So they can be less dangerous.''

''We can learn other things too,'' said Mr Quevedo. ''We can learn where the earth's riches are. If there's oil in West Africa, there must also be oil in Brazil. We know that Antarctica once had rich woods full of trees – so there must be oil under Antarctica.''

Juan said, ''If we want to enjoy the earth, we must learn to understand it.''

# A Crossword

Do you like crosswords? Here's one for you. Find the answers to the questions and write the answers in the boxes. Some of the answers go *across* from left to right. Some of them go *down* the page.

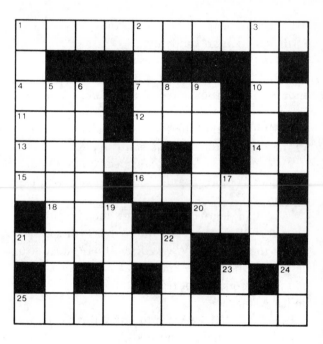

## Across

1 There was one at Yungay, in Peru, on May 31st 1970. (10)

4 The South American plate _____ only move to the west. (3)

7 People _____ a pen to write a letter. (3)

10 "I _____ hungry," said the boy. "I want to eat." (2)

11 The boy _____ his dinner, so, for a while, he wasn't hungry. (3)

12 "This boy is my _____," said Sam's father. (3)

13 The heavier Nazca sea _____ is moving down under Peru. (5)

14 "I've visited the volcano _____ Arequipa," said Juan. (2)

15 You have one at each side of your head. (3)

16 The girl _____ all her money on chocolate, so she couldn't pay for her bus ticket. (5)

18 Not old. (3)

20 You walk through the _____ and get into the garden. (4)

21 The _____ man carried three heavy boxes. (6)

25 "_____ all over the world are working on the question of earthquakes," said Mr Quevedo. (10)

## Down

1 "As the rock of the Nazca plate moves deeper under the earth, it becomes hotter and changes to liquid. Air and water _____ from it, and it breaks into pieces. (6)

2 People live in these. (6)

3 This volcano erupted in Indonesia in 1883. (8)

5 This ocean is between the Americas and Africa. (8)

6 The moon is _____ to the earth than the sun. (6)

8 The child was tired _____ he slept. (2)

9 When the child was asleep, his mother _____ the story. (5)

17 Not yes. (2)

19 The woman _____ her new dress for the party. (4)

22 "You must _____ off the bus at the cinema," the father told his daughter. (3)

23 "Your grandmother _____ waiting for you outside the cinema." (2)

24 "You will see her _____ the bus stops." (2)

# Answers

**Across**

1 earthquake 4 can 7 use 10 am 11 ate
12 son 13 plate 14 at 15 ear 16 spent
18 new 20 door 21 strong 25 scientists

**Down**

1 escape 2 houses 3 Krakatoa 5 Atlantic
6 nearer 8 so 9 ended 17 no 19 wore
22 get 23 is 24 as